GRANDAD & me

JOURNALS®
of a LIFETIME
made with love *from you to me*

www.JournalsOfALifetime.com

GRANDAD & Me

GRANDAD & Me will take you on an interactive and fun journey, having a great time getting to know each other better.

Tips to enjoy GRANDAD & Me :

- Your questions are in gold. Grandad's questions are in grey.

- Dip in and complete your questions in any order, whenever you want.

- Use words, drawings, doodles ... whatever feels right for you.

- There are no right or wrong answers, just your own.

- Use the extra pages to capture anything else you would like to explore.

- Agree when and how to share your pages with the other person.

- Enjoy yourself and have fun!

A bit about Grandad . . .

My full name :

My age :   Today's Date :

A picture of Grandad . . . a drawing or photo

GRANDAD

A bit about Me . . .

My full name :

My age :   Today's date :

A picture of Me . . . a drawing or photo

Me

A bit about Grandad . . .

What I love watching on television :

Best films :

Top Songs :

Favourite places :

Things I say a lot :

I love to eat :

GRANDAD

A bit about Me . . .

What I love watching on television :

Best films :

Top songs :

Favourite places :

Things I say a lot :

I love to eat :

Me

Today . . .

Who I talked to :

What I did :

The best things :

The worst things :

What I wanted to do, but didn't get around to :

GRANDAD

Today . . .

Who I talked to :

What I did :

The best things :

The worst things :

What I wanted to do, but didn't get around to :

Me

When I was younger . . .

My earliest memory :

What I was like :

When I was younger I thought that :

When I was younger . . .

My earliest memory :

What I was like :

When I was younger I thought that :

Me

Happened to me . . .

Funny things :

Embarrassing things :

Sad things :

GRANDAD

Happened to me . . . .

Funny things :

Embarrassing things :

Sad things :

Me

The way we are . . .

The ways we are similar :

The ways we are different :

Things I admire about you :

GRANDAD

The way we are . . .

The ways we are similar :

The ways we are different :

Things I admire about you :

Me

My family . . .

Some great memories of our family :

What I love about our family :

What I would like to be different :

GRANDAD

My family . . .

Some great memories of our family :

What I love about our family :

What I would like to be different :

Me

Family times . . .

Things I love doing with my family :

I wish we could :

I wish we didn't :

GRANDAD

Family times . . .

Things I love doing with my family :

I wish we could :

I wish we didn't :

Me

Where I live . . .

What I remember about the places I have lived :

Things at home that are special :

Where I might like to live in the future :

GRANDAD

Where I live . . .

What I remember about the places I have lived :

Things at home that are special :

Where I might like to live in the future :

Me

Birthdays . . .

My best memories :

How I would like to spend future birthdays :

My perfect present would be :

GRANDAD

Birthdays . . .

My best memories :

How I would like to spend future birthdays :

My perfect present would be :

Me

Holidays . . .

My best memories :

The best places I have been :

Where I would love to visit :

GRANDAD

Holidays . . .

My best memories :

The best places I have been :

Where I would love to visit :

Me

With friends . . .

How I feel about my friends :

What I admire most about you and your friends :

What I want to change about my friendships :

GRANDAD

With friends . . .

How I feel about my friends :

What I admire most about you and your friends :

What I want to change about my friendships :

Me

Messages for my friends . . .

To:

To:

To:

To:

To:

To:

GRANDAD

Messages for my friends . . .

To:

To:

To:

To:

To:

To:

Me

My Spare time . . .

What I enjoy doing most in my spare time :

What I would love to do :

What I love watching you do :

GRANDAD

My spare time . . .

What I enjoy doing most in my spare time :

What I would love to do :

What I love you watching me do :

Me

School . . .

What I loved about being at school :

What I found most difficult :

With the benefit of hindsight :

GRANDAD

School . . .

What I love about being at school :

What I find most difficult :

My greatest learning experience :

Me

Learning . . .

What I would love to learn :

How I best like to learn :

The help I would like from you :

GRANDAD

Learning . . .

What I would love to learn :

How I best like to learn :

The help I would like from you :

Me

Books & stories . . .

Some of my favourite books :

Books I love that I hope you will read :

Books I would love to read :

GRANDAD

Books & stories . . .

Some of my favourite books :

Favourite characters from my books :

Books I would love to read :

Me

Some of my favourite things . . .

GRANDAD

Some of my favourite things . . .

Me

Growing up . . .

What was exciting :

What I was concerned about :

The help and guidance I received :

GRANDAD

Growing up . . .

What is exciting :

What I am concerned about :

The help I would like :

Me

My body . . .

How I feel about me :

What I like about me :

What I would like to share with you :

GRANDAD

My body . . .

How I feel about me :

What I like about me :

What I would like to share with you :

Me

Being healthy . . .

A drawing of my ideas to be fit and healthy :

GRANDAD

Being healthy . . .

A drawing of my ideas to be fit and healthy :

Me

Feeling happy . . .

The things that make me happy :

What makes me feel confident :

Who I love spending time with :

GRANDAD

Feeling happy . . .

The things that make me happy :

What makes me feel confident :

Who I love spending time with :

Me

Feeling Sad . . .

The things that make me sad :

What knocks my confidence :

What helps me when I feel sad :

GRANDAD

Feeling sad . . .

The things that make me sad :

What knocks my confidence :

What helps me when I feel sad :

Me

My worries . . .

Things that worry me :

Some of my regrets :

How I best manage any worries :

GRANDAD

My worries . . .

Things that worry me :

Some of my regrets :

How I best manage any worries :

Me

Falling in love . . .

My views on love :

What is important to me :

My first love and what I learned :

GRANDAD

Falling in love . . .

My views on love :

What is important to me :

What I have learnt so far :

Me

My future . . .

Things I want to do in my life :

Things I want to do with you :

Some words to describe the person I want to be :

GRANDAD

My future . . .

Things I want to do in my life :

Things I want to do with you :

Some words to describe the person I want to be :

Me

My dreams . . .

What I dream about :

How I see my future :

What I wish I could spend more time doing :

GRANDAD

My dreams . . .

What I dream about :

How I see my future :

What I wish I could spend more time doing :

Me

Grandad & Me . . .

What I love about you :

What I love about us :

What I wish we could do more of :

GRANDAD

Me & Grandad . . .

What I love about you :

What I love about us :

What I wish we could do more of :

Me

Thoughts I have . . .

In 5 years :

I hope :

Something you don't know about me :

GRANDAD

Thoughts I have . . .

In 5 years :

I hope :

Something you don't know about me :

Me

Helping others . . .

People I admire who help others :

How I like to help others :

What I could do more :

GRANDAD

Helping others . . .

People I admire who help others :

How I like to help others :

What I could do more :

Me

Topics of Grandad's choice . . .

These pages are for you, Grandad, to write questions . . .

GRANDAD

Topics of Grandad's choice . . .

. . . or topics for you and your grandchild to answer

Me

Topics of my choice . . .

These pages are for you to write questions . . .

GRANDAD

Topics of my choice . . . .

. . . or topics for you and your grandad to answer

Me

A poem about me & you . . .

GRANDAD

A poem about me & you . . .

Me

A letter to myself based on what I
have discovered in this journal . . .

Dear Me

A letter to myself based on what I have discovered in this journal . . .

Dear Me

Me

Thinking about what I have discovered from this journal, here is a picture showing my dreams for the future . . .

GRANDAD

Thinking about what I have discovered from this journal, here is a picture showing my dreams for the future . . .

Me

Final thoughts & doodles . . .

Final thoughts & doodles . . .

Me

GRANDAD & me

First published in the UK by *from you to me* February 2015. Reprinted January 2018.
Copyright from you to me limited 2014

ISBN 978-1-907048-61-6

Printed and bound in China by Imago.
This paper is manufactured from pulp sourced from forests that are legally and sustainably managed.

For more information please contact:

from you to me
The Old Brewery
Newtown
Bradford on Avon
BA15 1NF, UK

hello@fromyoutome.com
www.JournalsOfALifetime.com